Born to a Kree mother and human father, former U.S. Air Force pilot **CAROL DANVERS** became a super hero when a Kree device activated her latent powers. Now she's an Avenger and Earth's Mightiest Hero.

# CAPTAIN MARVEL

# THE NEW WORLD

Recently, Carol took on the role of the Kree Accuser and used the Universal Weapon to help save the galaxy from yet another alien invasion. Along the way, she discovered Lauri-Ell, her Kree half sister, and together they realized that it was Lauri-Ell, not Carol, who was destined to wear the mantle of Accuser.

Now Lauri-Ell is back in space as a warrior guardian of the united Kree-Skrull Empire, and Captain Marvel has returned to protect Earth. Which is good, 'cuz...it's about to need her.

## KELLY THOMPSON
Writer

## LEE GARBETT
Artist

## BELÉN ORTEGA
Flashback Artist [#23-25]

## TAMRA BONVILLAIN [#22] & ANTONIO FABELA [#23-26]
Color Artists

## VC's CLAYTON COWLES
Letterer

## JORGE MOLINA
Cover Art

## KAT GREGOROWICZ
Assistant Editor

## SARAH BRUNSTAD
Editor

## WIL MOSS
Senior Editor

Collection Editor: JENNIFER GRÜNWALD
Assistant Editor: DANIEL KIRCHHOFFER
Assistant Managing Editor: MAIA LOY
Assistant Managing Editor: LISA MONTALBANO
VP Production & Special Projects: JEFF YOUNGQUIST

Book Designers: STACIE ZUCKER & ADAM DEL RE with CLAYTON COWLES & NICK RUSSELL
SVP Print, Sales & Marketing: DAVID GABRIEL
Editor in Chief: C.B. CEBULSKI

CAPTAIN MARVEL VOL. 5: THE NEW WORLD. Contains material originally published in magazine form as CAPTAIN MARVEL (2019) #22-26. First printing 2021. ISBN 978-1-302-92595-6. Published by MARVEL WORLDWIDE, INC., a subsidiary of MARVEL ENTERTAINMENT, LLC. OFFICE OF PUBLICATION: 1290 Avenue of the Americas, New York, NY 10104. © 2021 MARVEL No similarity between any of the names, characters, persons, and/or institutions in this magazine with those of any living or dead person or institution is intended, and any such similarity which may exist is purely coincidental. Printed in Canada. KEVIN FEIGE, Chief Creative Officer; DAN BUCKLEY, President, Marvel Entertainment; JOE QUESADA, EVP & Creative Director; DAVID BOGART, Associate Publisher & SVP of Talent Affairs; TOM BREVOORT, VP, Executive Editor; NICK LOWE, Executive Editor, VP of Content, Digital Publishing; DAVID GABRIEL, VP of Print & Digital Publishing; JEFF YOUNGQUIST, VP of Production & Special Projects; ALEX MORALES, Director of Publishing Operations; DAN EDINGTON, Managing Editor; RICKEY PURDIN, Director of Talent Relations; JENNIFER GRÜNWALD, Senior Editor, Special Projects; SUSAN CRESPI, Production Manager; STAN LEE, Chairman Emeritus. For information regarding advertising in Marvel Comics or on Marvel.com, please contact Vit DeBellis, Custom Solutions & Integrated Advertising Manager, at vdebellis@marvel.com. For Marvel subscription inquiries, please call 888-511-5480. Manufactured between 2/26/2021 and 3/30/2021 by SOLISCO PRINTERS, SCOTT, QC, CANADA.

10 9 8 7 6 5 4 3 2 1

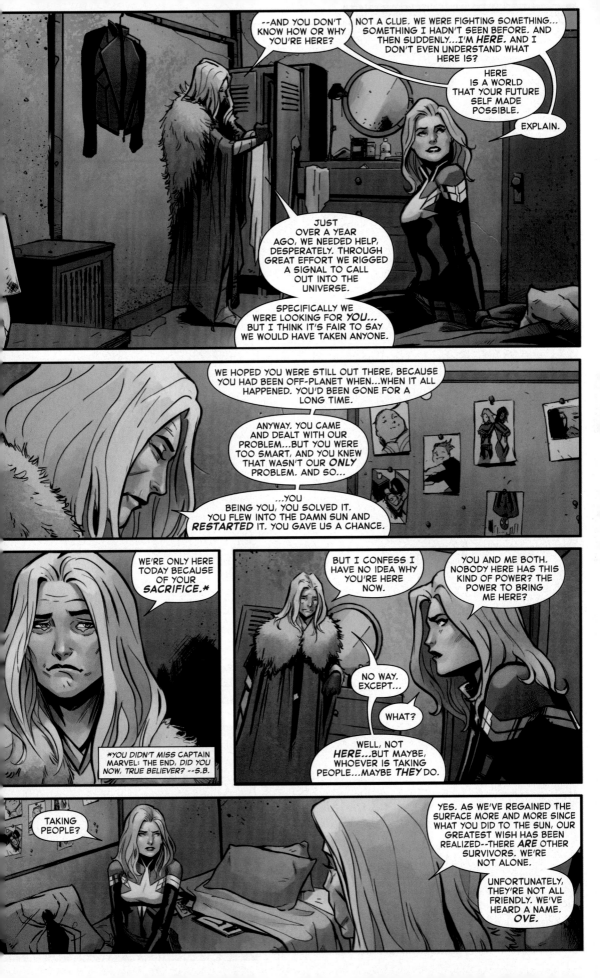

OKAY. THANKS FOR COMING, ALL OF YOU.

AS YOU MAY HAVE HEARD, RHODES WAS ABLE TO FOLLOW LUKE CAGE FOR SOME DISTANCE LAST NIGHT.

CAGE REMAINED ALONE AND APPEARED ALMOST AS IF HE WAS BEING *REMOTE PILOTED* FROM SOMEWHERE...

...WHICH TRACKS WITH HIS BIZARRE EMOTIONLESS BEHAVIOR. WE'RE STILL GOING IN PRETTY BLIND THOUGH.

ANYONE WANT OUT?

YEAH. ME.

DENIED. ANYONE ELSE?

CAROL, YOU ABSOLUTE NIGHTMARE.

*PFFT.* YOU LOVE IT.

AM I LATE?

RIGHT ON TIME.

I DON'T HAVE *MJOLNIR.* IT WON'T COME TO ME.

OKAY.

YOU STILL WANT ME?

I DO.

THEN LET'S GO RESCUE OUR FRIENDS AND #$@% SOME #$@% UP.

THIS IS MY KIND OF TEAM.

THERE'S SOMETHING COMFORTING ABOUT THE FACT THAT EVEN IN A DYSTOPIAN NIGHTMARE, *THIS* HAS SURVIVED. THIS IS EVERYTHING.

EVERYTHING IS A MYSTERY. HOW I GOT HERE, WHY IT HAPPENED, IF IT CAN BE UNDONE. MY MIND RACES WORRYING ABOUT WHAT I LEFT BEHIND...MY LOVED ONES IN UNKNOWN DANGER.

THIS IS ALL HAPPENING SO FAST. I HAVEN'T EVEN BEEN HERE A DAY AND I'M LEADING A TEAM I DON'T KNOW INTO THE UNKNOWN.

BUT ALSO...THESE PEOPLE...THIS *WORLD* NEEDS HELP. WHAT THEY'VE DONE IS INCREDIBLE, EVEN SURVIVING THIS LONG FEELS LIKE A MIRACLE. EVEN IF WE CAN WIN THE DAY AND FIND A WAY HOME FOR ME, CAN I REALLY JUST ABANDON THEM?

THE TRUTH IS...I DON'T KNOW.

WE'RE GETTING CLOSE. LET'S STOP AND REST.

UGH. FINALLY.

SO WHO'S GOING TO TELL ME WHAT HAPPENED HERE...HOW THINGS GOT TO THIS POINT?

WELL...MOST OF THIS CREW WERE BABIES, OR NOT EVEN BABIES, FOR A LOT OF IT, SO THAT LEAVES ME OR EMMA, *HUH?*

NOT IT.

WELL. THE WORLD'S ALWAYS ENDING, ISN'T IT? THERE'S ALWAYS ANOTHER END OF THE WORLD. THIS WAS JUST THE ONE WE *LOST.*

"SO AT FIRST THIS WAS MORE OF THE SAME. THE WORLD WAS ENDING THANKS TO SOME MYSTERIOUS, POSSIBLY ALIEN, FORCES BENT ON OUR DESTRUCTION. THE HEROES CAME TOGETHER, AS THEY DO.

"THE GOVERNMENT WAS CONSIDERING THE 'NUCLEAR OPTION,' AS THEY DO.

"WE HIT ALL THE CLASSIC BEATS.

"NOBODY KNEW WHERE THEY CAME FROM...OR WHAT THEY WANTED. WE FOUGHT TWO WARS, THINKING EACH WAS THE LAST.

"I... WE LOST KATE IN THE FIRST ONE. WE LOST SO MANY. MOST OF THE AVENGERS...THE X-MEN, THE INHUMANS, THE FANTASTIC FOUR, GUARDIANS, CHAMPIONS, RUNAWAYS... SO MANY.

"BUT AMID THE LOSS THERE WAS STILL HOPE. WE WERE ALIVE. WE HAD MADE IT THROUGH TO THE OTHER SIDE. WE HAD WON. WE BELIEVED IT WAS OVER.

"A LOT OF OUR PEOPLE WERE BORN BETWEEN THE TWO WARS...

"...KATIE BARTON...BRIGID... SORA...RHODES...IRENE LEBEAU... LUCY RAND...EVEN FANTOMEX 5... THOUGH 'BORN' IS MAYBE NOT THE RIGHT WORD IN HIS CASE.

"BUT THE SECOND WAR...WHEN IT CAME, IT CAME FAST AND FURIOUS. IT TOOK MOST OF THE REST OF THE HEROES.

"I THINK WHEN WE SAW THOR KILLED...

"...WE KNEW WE WERE TRULY LOST.

"WHAT NOBODY EXPECTED WAS THE *SICKNESS.* WE DIDN'T CONNECT IT TO THE WARS...THE INVASION AT FIRST. BUT EVENTUALLY IT SEEMED OBVIOUS.

"WE STILL DON'T KNOW WHAT HAPPENED. IT DECIMATED WHAT WAS LEFT. SCATTERED US TO THE WINDS.

"AND THEN THE BUTTON.

"WE ARGUED HARD AGAINST IT, OF COURSE. BUT PETTY FRIGHTENED MEN HAVE HEAVY FINGERS. TALE AS OLD AS TIME.

"SOMETIMES I THINK THEY PUSHED THE BUTTON OUT OF SPITE.

"IF WE COULDN'T HAVE THE WORLD, THEN NO ONE WOULD.

"WE WENT UNDERGROUND.

"WE ONLY SURVIVED BECAUSE OF HEROES PUSHING THEMSELVES TO THE ABSOLUTE LIMIT.

"ARMOR KEPT HER SHIELD UP AROUND OUR GROUP FOR OVER A YEAR WITHOUT DROPPING IT. IT ALMOST KILLED HER.

"HAZMAT ABSORBED AND REDIRECTED RADIATION...CREATING POCKETS ON THE SURFACE WHERE THE MOST RESILIENT OF US COULD SURVIVE...FOR A TIME.

"SPIDER-WOMAN... SHE VENTURED OUT INTO THE NUCLEAR WASTELAND LOOKING FOR RESOURCES... FOR SURVIVORS. HER IMMUNITY TO RADIATION PROTECTED HER. BUT SHE PUSHED IT TOO FAR. IT ALMOST KILLED HER TOO.

"OTHERS WERE NOT SO LUCKY. MAGNETO DIED PROTECTING US...BUILDING THE UNDERGROUND WHERE WE STILL LIVE TODAY.

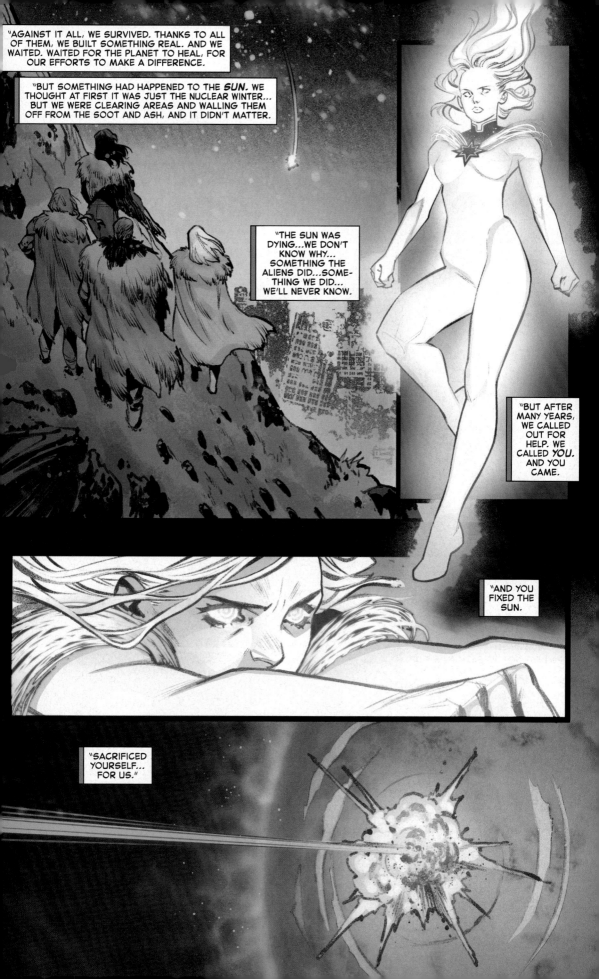

"AGAINST IT ALL, WE SURVIVED. THANKS TO ALL OF THEM, WE BUILT SOMETHING REAL. AND WE WAITED. WAITED FOR THE PLANET TO HEAL, FOR OUR EFFORTS TO MAKE A DIFFERENCE.

"BUT SOMETHING HAD HAPPENED TO THE *SUN.* WE THOUGHT AT FIRST IT WAS JUST THE NUCLEAR WINTER... BUT WE WERE CLEARING AREAS AND WALLING THEM OFF FROM THE SOOT AND ASH, AND IT DIDN'T MATTER.

"THE SUN WAS DYING...WE DON'T KNOW WHY... SOMETHING THE ALIENS DID...SOMETHING WE DID... WE'LL NEVER KNOW.

"BUT AFTER MANY YEARS, WE CALLED OUT FOR HELP. WE CALLED *YOU.* AND YOU CAME.

"AND YOU FIXED THE SUN.

"SACRIFICED YOURSELF... FOR US."

"WHEN THE FIRST ASSAULTS THAT EVENTUALLY ENDED HUMAN CIVILIZATION BEGAN, MY FATHER OFFERED HIS HELP TO THE HUMANS, AS HE HAD MANY TIMES BEFORE.

"HE JOINED THE HEROES IN THEIR BATTLES, TRYING VALIANTLY TO SAVE THE EARTH.

"AT FIRST.

"BUT SOMETIME BETWEEN THE FIRST WAR AND THE SECOND--AND FORGIVE ME FOR BEING LIGHT ON DETAILS, I WAS NOT YET BORN--HE GREW DISSATISFIED WITH WHAT HE SAW.

"I CAN NEVER KNOW HIS MIND FOR CERTAIN, BUT OTHERS SAY THAT HE SAW IN THE TRAGEDY A DESTINY OF SORTS. THAT THE HUMANS COULD NOT SURVIVE THIS LATEST THREAT, AND THAT HIS PEOPLE--*HIS* KINGDOM--*COULD.*

"*ATLANTIS* COULD SURVIVE.

"HE MADE PREPARATIONS TO ENSURE THE SURVIVAL OF HIS PEOPLE. SO THAT SOMEDAY HIS PROGENY WOULD HAVE A KINGDOM TO INHERIT.

"AND AS YOU NOW KNOW, THE HUMANS DID LOSE THEIR WAR.

"AND SO ATLANTIS SURVIVED...SOME MIGHT SAY *THRIVED.*

"FOR ALL THAT WE ATLANTEANS HAVE GREAT AND SOMETIMES MISPLACED AFFECTION FOR HUMANS, THE TRUTH IS THAT THEY WERE DESTROYING THIS PLANET AT INCREDIBLE SPEED.

"AND WHEN THEY WERE NO LONGER AROUND IN GREAT NUMBERS TO POLLUTE AND PILLAGE AND DESTROY, ATLANTIS WAS HEALTHIER AND STRONGER THAN EVER.

"BUT THE WORLD DOES NOT LOVE A VACUUM.

"IT SEEKS TO FILL...

"...WITH WHATEVER IT CAN.

"I WAS FIVE WHEN I FIRST LEARNED THAT THERE WERE PEOPLE WHO DID NOT LOVE MY FATHER. WHEN THEY TRIED TO MURDER HIM IN HIS OWN HOME.

"'A ROGUE FACTION,' MY MOTHER CALLED IT, AND 'NO BOTHER TO ROYALTY LIKE US.'

"THEY WERE DEALT WITH ACCORDINGLY.

"BUT THAT WAS THE MOMENT WHEN I BECAME AWARE THAT LIFE MIGHT NOT ALWAYS BE SO EASY AND BLESSED.

"THE 'ROGUE FACTION' GREW, AND BY THE TIME I WAS A YOUNG MAN OF 15, IT WAS A GENUINE REBELLION.

"WHEN I WAS 16, I WATCHED THE REBELLION MURDER MY FATHER.

"MY MOTHER AND I BARELY ESCAPED WITH OUR LIVES.

"BUT WITH NAMOR DEAD AND THE REBELLION NOW IN CONTROL, WE WERE MARKED. NOWHERE IN THE SEA WAS SAFE--NOR ASGARD, FOR MOTHER WAS NO LONGER WELCOME THERE.

"SO WE EXILED OURSELVES TO THE SURFACE.

"FORTUNATELY, WE WERE STRONG, AND SO THE DANGEROUS CONDITIONS-- THE REMAINING RADIATION AND THE ICE--WERE PROBLEMS FOR US, BUT NOT INSURMOUNTABLE ONES.

"WE BEGAN BUILDING A SIMPLE LIFE.

"IT WAS ONLY WHEN WE FOUND OTHER POWERFUL SURVIVORS, LIKE JOLT AND CRYSTAL, THAT I REALIZED WHAT WE COULD DO ON THE SURFACE. HOW WE COULD *REBUILD*.

"I HAD LOST THE SEA...MY HOMELAND...BUT *HERE* I COULD BUILD SOMETHING *NEW*.

"SOMETHING MY FATHER WOULD BE PROUD OF.

"IT WAS THE ONLY WAY TO COME OUT FROM HIS MAGNIFICENT SHADOW.

"TO BECOME MY OWN MAN. A *GREAT* ONE."

I CAN'T BELIEVE YOU'RE STILL WEARING THE DRESS FOR RECON.

CAROL, I HAVE FOUGHT WARS IN LESS. AND DIDN'T YOU USED TO WEAR A SWIMSUIT WITH THIGH HIGHS? YOU KNOW WHAT THEY SAY ABOUT STONES AND GLASS HOUSES?

YOU GUYS REMEMBER WE'RE TELEPATHICALLY LINKED, RIGHT?

AREN'T YOU ALL LUCKY, MY LOVES.

NOTHING TO REPORT SO FAR ON THE MAIN LEVEL. ALL'S QUIET. BUT PERHAPS TOO QUIET?

IT'S NOT A HORROR MOVIE, JOHNNY.

KATIE, YOU'VE NEVER EVEN SEEN A HORROR MOVIE.

NEITHER HAVE YOU...BUT WE CAN STILL KNOW WHAT THEY ARE.

YOU GUYS ARE ALL VERY BAD AT THIS.

PLEASE LET US NEVER LINK MINDS AGAIN.

ALL CLEAR SO FAR ON THE UPPER LEVEL. I'M WITH WHOEVER SAID THIS FEELS LIKE A HORROR MOVIE. AND I HAVE SEEN ONE.

WELL, THIS LOOKS OMINOUS.

MAYBE. BUT I'M SURE WE'RE BEING MONITORED DESPITE HIS CASUAL APPROACH.

HE'S CONFIDENT... ARROGANT. HE'S NOT AFRAID OF US OR WHAT WE MIGHT DO. AND I DON'T LIKE THAT.

AGREED. LET'S BREAK IN ANYWAY.

WE'RE ALL EN ROUTE TO YOUR LOCATION.

IT'S VERY NAUGHTY OF YOU TO BE SNEAKING AROUND AT NIGHT AND BOTHERING ALL MY FAVORITE TREASURES. I THINK YOU AND YOUR PEOPLE WILL HAVE TO BE PUNISHED. DON'T YOU AGREE, MOTHER?

I AM AFRAID I DO, SON.

ENCHANTRESS. INCREDIBLY POWERFUL ASGARDIAN SORCERESS. APPARENTLY OVE'S MOTHER.

COME, MY TREASURES. COME AND HURT THEM TERRIBLY. HURT THEM UNTIL THEY STOP GETTING UP, AND THEN THEY WILL BECOME MY TREASURES TOO.

BE EXTRA CAREFUL WITH THE SHINY ONE IN RED, YELLOW AND BLUE. SHE'S SPECIAL.

AS YOU WISH.

EVERYTHING HURTS. HOW LONG WAS I OUT? HAVE TO ASSUME THE ONLY REASON LUKE AND ENCHANTRESS DIDN'T KILL ME IS BECAUSE THEY NEED ME FOR SOMETHING.

THEY'VE SEPARATED ME FROM THE OTHERS. AND BOUND ME TO SOME KIND OF... *ALTAR?*

WHATEVER THEY'RE PLANNING ISN'T A PARTY.

DID I MAKE A HORRIBLE MISTAKE? HAVE I KILLED US ALL?

I HAVE SO MANY PLANS FOR ALL MY LOVELY NEW TREASURES, CAROL. I CAN'T THANK YOU ENOUGH FOR BRINGING THEM TO ME. THEY'RE JUST RIFE WITH POSSIBILITIES.

NONE AS OBVIOUS AS ARMOR, JOLT AND CRYSTAL OF COURSE...BUT HAVE NO FEAR--WE WILL FIND A USE FOR EACH AND EVERY ONE OF THEM IN PARADISE, I ASSURE YOU.

BUT YOU. YOU'RE DIFFERENT, AREN'T YOU? YOU'RE UNSTUCK FROM TIME. YOU'RE SPECIAL.

YOU'RE THE KEY TO MY *FUTURE*, CAROL.

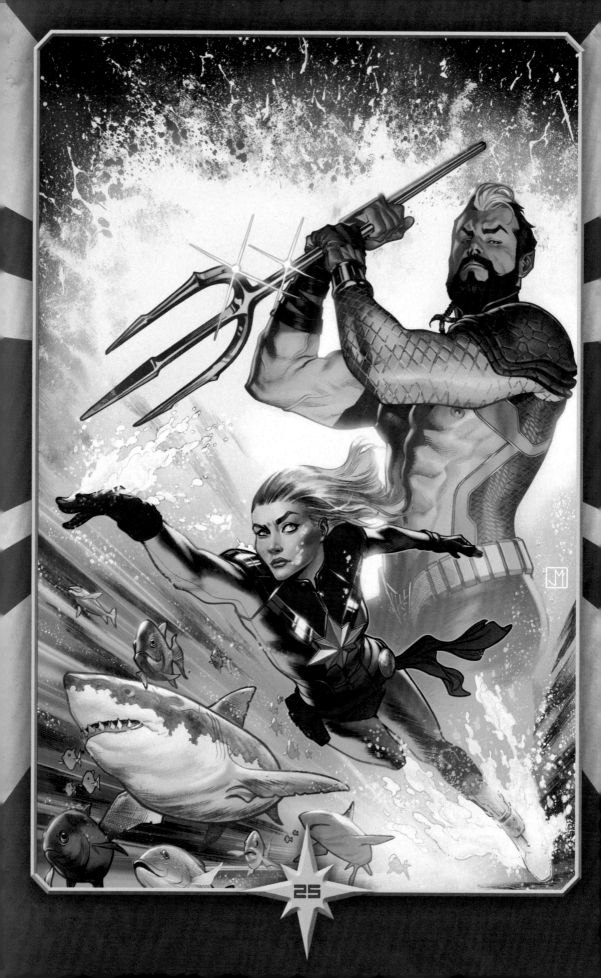

RHODES! I... JUST TALKING TO MYSELF. CAN YOU FREE ME?

I DON'T KNOW. THE MAGIC MAKES IT TRICKY TO PICK A LOCK.

I THINK WE BOTH KNOW YOU CAN DO MORE THAN PICK LOCKS.

I... IT DOESN'T ALWAYS WORK WHEN I *PHASE* PEOPLE WHO AREN'T ME, BRIGID.

...IT WILL HURT, TOO.

WHAT DOESN'T?

BUT IT WILL. IT MUST, RHODES.

TRY NOT TO SCREAM.

HNNNG.

"...FOR HE IS ME, CAPTAIN, AND HE IS HIS FATHER, AND SO HE IS MEANT TO RULE NO MATTER WHAT WE MAY OTHERWISE DESIRE.

"TO BE HONEST, EXCEPT FOR HOW HANDSOME HE WAS, I NEVER THOUGHT MUCH OF *NAMOR.*

"WELL, UNTIL THE END OF THE WORLD, WHICH HAD THE MISFORTUNE TO HAPPEN WHILE I WAS TRAPPED ON MIDGARD.

"HE SUDDENLY SEEMED VERY APPEALING. THE SURFACE WORLD WAS A DISASTER, WHILE UNDER THE SEA *HE* HAD A WHOLE WORLD TO RULE...

"...AND MAYBE EVEN MORE WHEN THE WAR WAS OVER.

"HE WAS POWERFUL AND CHARMING.

"AND AS I AM BOTH THOSE THINGS MYSELF...I CONVINCED MYSELF IT WAS A REASONABLE MATCH.

"I SUSPECT HE DID THE SAME.

"I ESCAPED WITH OVE IN THE NIGHT, LIKE CRIMINALS. I EXILED US TO THE SURFACE BEFORE THE ATLANTEANS COULD KILL MY SON FOR HIS TREACHERY.

"HE WAS ALL I HAD LEFT TO LOVE IN ALL THE WORLDS.

"I USED TO RULE IN SUCH GLORY AND SPLENDOR, DANCING BETWEEN REALMS WITH SUCH EFFORTLESS GRACE. I COULD BE ANYONE AND ANYTHING.

"NOW, TRAPPED ON THIS DEAD ROCK...HE WAS MY ONLY JOY.

"HE IS PERHAPS A MONSTER. BUT HE IS STILL MINE..."

MAHMUD ASRAR
26 VARIANT

BOOM

BEEN WANTING TO HIT THIS GUY FOR WHAT FEELS LIKE A WEEK.

IT'S PERHAPS TACKY TO REVEL IN IT...

...BUT IT FEELS GLORIOUS.

AND WE'RE JUST GETTING STARTED.

KRAK

WOULD LOVE TO REALLY UNLEASH THE FULL WEIGHT OF THIS *POWER* BRIGID CHARGED ME UP WITH...BUT ENOUGH FORCE TO EVEN SINGE OVE WILL LIKELY MEAN KILLING ALMOST EVERYONE ELSE HERE.

I NEED ANOTHER WAY.

THEY HAVEN'T DECIDED ON A NEW NAME FOR THE PLACE YET, BUT I SORT OF HOPE THEY JUST GO WITH PLAIN OLD *NEW YORK.* SOMETHING COMFORTING IN KNOWING THAT IT CAN RISE FROM THE ASHES...THAT IT CAN *SURVIVE.*

BRIGID HAS FALLEN INTO GODHOOD WITH EASE. IT SUITS HER. I ALWAYS KNEW IT WOULD.

AGREED. SHE'S A NATURAL.

GERRY SAYS DANI'S JUST ARRIVED WITH THE LAST OF OUR PEOPLE. YOU SHOULD GO DOWN THERE AND STOP SULKING.

I'M NOT SULKING, JESS. I'M MAD.

ARE THOSE DIFFERENT?

C'MON. I HELPED SAVE THE DAY HERE, AND THAT'S INCREDIBLE, BUT ULTIMATELY I FAILED.

OVE DID EXACTLY WHAT HE WANTED. I'VE UNLEASHED HIM ON OUR PAST--AND WHO KNOWS WHAT HE'S DOING THERE.

CAN'T BE THAT BAD SINCE WE'RE ALL STILL HERE, RIGHT?

PERHAPS.

HOW ARE JOLT AND CRYSTAL DOING?

MUCH BETTER.

AND HISAKO?

HEY NOW. YOU'RE LESS SHINY. STILL A BIT GLOWY... YOU DEFINITELY CAN'T GO TO THE MOVIES OR ANYTHING CRAZY, BUT IT'S BETTER.

ARE YOU CONTROLLING THAT, OR...?

NO. I THINK IT'S JUST FADING ON ITS OWN.

WELL, YOU MIGHT WANT TO LOOK INTO THAT...BOTH SO YOU CAN USE IT FOR DEFEATING WEIRD TENTACLE MONSTERS AND ALSO SO THAT YOU CAN GO TO THE MOVIES WITHOUT GETTING POPCORN THROWN AT YOUR HEAD.

HEH. YEAH. GOOD POINT.

WHAT'S GOING ON, CAROL? TALK TO ME.

I...I WANT TO BE VERY CLEAR ABOUT THIS WITH YOU...

BUT...IN THE FUTURE, I MET YOUR DAUGHTER.

WHAT?

I MET HER AND SHE'S INCREDIBLE. GOD, RHODEY, YOU'D BE SO PROUD. SHE'S SMART AND STRONG AND BEAUTIFUL AND SO DAMN GOOD, JUST LIKE YOU...

I AM HEAD OVER HEELS IN LOVE WITH YOU, RHODEY. I HAVE BEEN FOR A LONG TIME. WE DON'T SAY IT A LOT, BUT IT NEEDS TO BE SAID.

I FEEL A *"BUT"* COMING?

...AND SHE WASN'T *MINE*.

AND WE... WE HAVE TO BREAK UP.

IT'S ALL I CAN THINK ABOUT, THIS DAUGHTER... MAYBE SHE'S IN YOUR FUTURE AND MAYBE NOT...

...BUT IF THERE'S EVEN THE SLIGHTEST CHANCE THAT SHE IS, THEN EVERY MINUTE YOU'RE WITH ME...

...I'M STANDING IN THE WAY OF THAT INCREDIBLE PERSON BEING BORN.

AND I... IT'S WRONG. I JUST CAN'T LIVE WITH THAT...OR WITH MYSELF. Y-YOUR FUTURE...IT ISN'T WITH ME, AND I HAVE TO GET OUT OF THE WAY.

AND I HAVE NO SAY IN THIS?

I...

YOU'RE THROWING AWAY OUR RELATIONSHIP OVER THE CHANCE THAT SOME POSSIBLE FUTURE YOU EXPERIENCED WAS REAL?

SHE WAS REAL, RHODEY... AND I CAN'T FORGET HER.

CAROL, THIS IS INSANE. DO YOU KNOW HOW INSANE THIS SOUNDS?

A FEW HOURS AGO WE WERE PLANNING OUR FIRST REAL VACATION, AND NOW WE'RE BREAKING UP OVER A POSSIBLE FUTURE THAT MIGHT NEVER HAPPEN?

IF YOU HAD MET HER... WHEN YOU MEET HER, YOU'LL UNDERSTAND--

I WOULDN'T COUNT ON IT.

Y-YOU'RE GOING?

I HAVE TO GET OUT OF HERE. I HAVE TO THINK.

WHEN YOU MEET HER, YOU'LL UNDERSTAND... YOU'LL UNDERSTAND AND YOU'LL FORGIVE ME.

NEXT: CRASH & BURN!

**ADI GRANOV**
22 VARIANT

**RUSSELL DAUTERMAN**
23 VARIANT

**TAURIN CLARKE**
22 HORROR VARIANT

**TRADD MOORE**
24 KNULLIFIED VARIANT

**JUANN CABAL & MATTHEW WILSON**
25 STORMBREAKERS VARIANT

**EMA LUPACCHINO & DAVID CURIEL**
26 MASTERWORKS VARIANT